W
CELI

Ghost Stories

Prepare to be frightened by these terrifying tales from
well-known characters from or with connections to Wales

South Wales Paranormal Research

BRADWELL
BOOKS

Published by Bradwell Books
9 Orgreave Close Sheffield S13 9NP
Email: books@bradwellbooks.co.uk

British Library Cataloguing in Publication Data: a catalogue
record for this book is available from the British Library.

1st Edition

ISBN: 9781909914261

Print: Gomer Press, Llandysul, Ceredigion SA44 4JL
Design by: jenksdesign@yahoo.co.uk
Photograph Credits: All supplied by
South Wales Paranormal Research unless otherwise indicated
Front cover: Caerphilly Castle, supplied by the
South Wales Paranormal Research
Back cover: iStock

For Kevin
and in memory of **Tina Laurent**

CONTENTS

INTRODUCTION

Over the last few years South Wales Paranormal Research (SWPR) has worked with the Cystic Fibrosis Trust in helping them to raise much-needed funds to help battle against cystic fibrosis.

The rich variety of stories provided in our earlier books seemed to indicate that most people have a paranormal story to tell, or have at some point visited a spooky location which has left an impression. This gave us the idea of a book entirely made up of 'true' ghost stories experienced by Welsh personalities or those associated with Wales in some way.

We would like to thank all of the story-tellers, their representatives and agents for helping us to provide the stories contained in this book. We have collected a great many in recent years, all of which have been donated to us to help raise money for the Cystic Fibrosis Trust.

Not everyone believes in ghosts, indeed not all of our contributors believe in ghosts, but almost everyone enjoys a good ghost story. These are some of our favourites. We hope that you will enjoy them.

Support from the South Wales Paranormal Research is particularly special as the Trust is marking its 50th year, but we are not celebrating but redoubling our efforts! The average life expectancy for someone with cystic fibrosis is 40. We are hoping that with fundraising like this we can fund research into better treatment for those with the condition. We are committed to improving the lives of those with cystic fibrosis so that they can see their 50th birthday and beyond.

Carolyn Holt
The Cystic Fibrosis Trust's Fundraising Manager for Wales

Cystic Fibrosis grateful for your support

CASTLES AND STATELY HOMES

ROY NOBLE – Tredegar House

Roy is well known for his extremely popular programmes on BBC Radio Wales. His story concerns Tredegar House.

My wife Elaine and I had joined a ghost evening at Tredegar House, Newport, because a colleague of mine, a poet from Newport, doubled up as a guide for such occasions. I had

Tredegar House, one-time home of an influential family whose members included Viscount Evan Morgan well known for his fascination with black magic. Tredegar's most famous ghost is a lady in white sometimes thought to be Gwyneth, the sister of Evan.

visited Tredegar House, associated with the Morgan family of Captain Morgan fame, some years before and had heard tales of spookiness from the staff there. Sometimes, doors that were closed before lock-up at the end of the day were found to be open the following morning.

Our ghost tour went entertainingly well and when we got to the top floor, we were given divining rods. These rods were supposed to react when they got to so called ghost hot-spots in the rooms. We were divided into two groups and in one room our divining rods were swaying all over the place, except for the ones held by Elaine. She regarded herself as a sceptic and held her rods in a firm grip.

Suddenly, we heard a crash and screams coming from the other group in the adjoining room. We all rushed in to meet the other group rushing out. When everyone got control of themselves again, they told us that, in their bedroom, the hand-held divining rods were also swaying uncontrollably, so one of the group said firmly, and loudly, 'If there's anyone here, show us a sign . . . go on, show us a sign' . . . and in the next breath, the bed collapsed. No one was near it when it crashed to the floor. For the rest of the tour, both groups huddled closely, with everyone quietly pushing and jostling, so that they wouldn't be last as we made our way downstairs.

SIR RODDY LLEWELLYN – Sausmarez Manor

Over the years, Sir Roddy Llewellyn has written and broadcast on various topics relating to horticulture and heritage and he now runs his own Garden Design company based in the Cotswolds. Inevitably these activities have brought him into contact with a variety of interesting and ancient historic properties.

Sir Roddy has previously concluded that he has no great sensitivity to these types of paranormal activities and says

Sausmarez manor is an ancient building which has been much altered over the years. Parts of the manor date from the early 13th or late 12th centuries.
Copyright © Image Courtesy of VisitGuernsey

that he has yet to witness anything ghostly himself. However, some family members are quite convinced that they have had paranormal experiences. One of Sir Roddy's childhood homes was in Llanvihangel Gobion in Wales. Sir Roddy's mother, the Hon. Christine Saumarez (who was always known as 'Teeny') believed that the house was haunted and was able to recount several instances of ghostly activity.

Teeny was a descendant of the important historical figure Admiral Sir James Saumarez, who at one point in his career served on board the HMS *Victory* and was to become second-in-command to Horatio Nelson at the Battle of the Nile. The Saumarez family have long been associated with the Island of Guernsey and the family still own Sausmarez Manor on the island.

Sausmarez Manor has the reputation of being a very haunted house. Most of the ghosts at the manor are friendly and span the full historical period of the building. One of the most interesting hauntings relates to a previous occupant who only died in the last 30 years. Sir Roddy was able to tell us the story of this most recent of ghosts, who is thought to be the spirit of one of his own relations on his mother's side of the family: Cecil De Sausmarez, who was a previous Seigneur (Lord of the Manor). Apparently the current Seigneur, Sir Roddy's cousin, has been known to hear the voice of Cecil coming from the hallways of the house. It is said that Cecil can be heard relating some of his favourite stories as if conducting a tour of The Manor for visitors, just as he would have done so frequently in his own lifetime.

ELIN MANAHAN THOMAS – Craig y Nos

Elin is a soprano who regularly appears on television and in concert performances. Elin is also a recording artist and appeared in the opening ceremony of the London Paralympics seen by an audience of more than a billion viewers worldwide. Elin's story concerns the early Victorian mansion Craig y Nos. It relates to the end of the nineteenth century when the castle was owned and transformed by a leading opera star of the day.

*In 1840 Captain Rice Davies Powell came to Glyntawe and decided to build
a country house alongside the River Tawe in the upper reaches of the valley.*
Copyright © Image Courtesy of Brecknock Museum & Art Gallery

A few years ago I was recording a CD in Craig y Nos, in the wonderful theatre built by the famous opera singer from the turn of the century, Adelina Patti. The Italian diva had made her home in Wales after a stellar international career, singing for Verdi and other great names, and Craig y Nos was her crowning glory.

The recording team and I spent a few days there, and at the start of every session I'd turn up early to warm up, while the producer listened to the previous day's material in the editing room.

One morning, I breezed in at nine, and as I walked into the theatre I could hear a high soprano voice drifting through the walls. Presuming it to be some takes of myself from the previous day, I bounced into the editing room to say hello . . . But there was no one there. It was dark and cold and none of the recording team had even arrived yet. The machines weren't turned on. The singing, however, could still be clearly heard – beautiful, dulcet tones wafting around the theatre. I quickly opened the door onto the stage and rushed out to see if the voice was louder there, but quite abruptly it stopped. And the room was empty.

A few minutes later my producer arrived, and seeing me white as a sheet and gibbering about dead opera singers, he sent me off for strong, sweet tea and delayed the start of the session! I'll never know whether the voice I heard was that of Adelina Patti, luxuriating in the acoustics of her private theatre – from beyond the grave. But her presence certainly pervades Craig y Nos, and to this day, it has stayed with me too.

LIONEL FANTHORPE – Caerphilly Castle

Lionel is a popular radio presenter and is the author of more than 250 books. He is also a patron of SWPR.

When we were making the TV series *Castles of Horror* for the Discovery Channel, our visit to Caerphilly was one of the most memorable. The centuries have added an atmosphere of mystery to the enormous old castle. Even with a producer, director, film and sound crew working together to make that episode, there was an awesome sense of isolation and mystery within the ancient stones. It was as though actors

Caerphilly Castle: One of the biggest castles in the world

from bygone times were struggling to get into the film we were making. Caerphilly Castle most certainly has what every psychic investigator would refer to as 'atmosphere'.

Some psychical researchers and explorers of the anomalous have put forward the carefully considered hypothesis that a number of widely reported hauntings are associated with outbursts of emotional energy. Over and above the emotion which inevitably accompanies warfare and battle action, Caerphilly Castle was the scene of powerful romantic emotion, as well as fiendish jealousy and revenge. Gilbert de Clare, the builder of the castle, was married to the exquisitely beautiful Princess Alice of Angoulême, a marriage that had almost certainly been arranged for political reasons rather than love. Inexplicably, Gilbert was more attracted by warfare than by his beautiful and passionate young wife, who was often left alone while he rode off to battle. In her loneliness, Alice met and fell in love with a dashing and handsome Welsh Prince, Gruffudd of Brithdir. Understandably, Gruffudd was equally attracted to Alice and they soon became lovers.

Unfortunately, Gruffudd suffered a twinge of conscience about their affair, and confessed what was going on to a monk. He turned out to be an untrustworthy wretch, who broke the seal of the confessional. The treacherous monk reported the affair to Gilbert. Furious with jealousy, he sent Alice back to France in disgrace.

Gruffudd found out what had happened and dealt with the treacherous monk appropriately – he hanged him. Not satisfied with sending Alice back to France, however, the vengeful Gilbert set out to find Gruffudd. When he finally caught up with the Prince of Brithdir, he also had him hanged. Word of her lover's death reached Alice in France. She had loved Gruffudd so much that she fell dead with shock and grief on hearing what had happened to him.

Many reliable witnesses have reported seeing Alice's ghost, dressed in a beautiful green gown, moving from one tower of Caerphilly Castle to another. It has been suggested by some investigators that the green of her sumptuous dress indicates the vengeful jealousy of Gilbert. She, herself, has been described as looking desperately grief-stricken, yet with an air of indestructible optimism as she looks out across the night – and across the centuries – for the return of her beloved Gruffudd.

CAT WEATHERILL – Rowton Castle

Cat Weatherill is a children's author and story-teller. She regularly performs at story-telling and literature festivals and specialises in ghost stories. Cat is part Welsh, and her story comes from just over the border at Rowton Castle.

As a professional ghost story teller, I hear many 'true' stories about ghosts. After every show, there will be at least one person who wants to share something – guaranteed! And I

Rowton Castle was in the Lyster family for 400 years. Later it spent many years as a college for the blind. In the mid 1980's it took on its current function as a hotel.

love to listen. My favourite story came from an antiques dealer who was renovating an ancient house somewhere in mid-Wales. He told me his efforts were being constantly hampered by a vengeful ghost who clearly disliked the attempted alterations to his domain.

One day, the dealer told me, he and a friend had struggled for hours to hang a massive oak door. The walls were so solid, it had taken for ever to get the fittings in, and it was only with a Herculean late-night effort that they managed to lift the door onto them. Finally they went to bed, totally exhausted.

When they came down the next morning, they found the door lying on the floor. The fittings had been removed from the wall and were arranged in a neat row beside it.

But nothing has ever happened to me. I have never seen a ghost – or have I? Maybe they are all around us, but only some people have the ability to see them. I honestly don't know.

I can remember only one occasion when I felt I was in the presence of something *otherworldly*. It was ten years ago, at Rowton Castle Hotel, when I was leading a group of guests around the castle on a late night ghost tour . . .

The building dates from the seventeenth century, and it is a perfect place to tell ghost stories. There are twisty staircases, dark corridors – and a haunted bedroom. I won't tell you what number it is, because I imagine the room is still regularly let to guests. It certainly was at that time – though according to the staff back then, the paranormal activity usually happened when the room was unoccupied. I stayed in the room once and found it unusually cold, despite the heating being on, but I didn't hear footsteps on the gravel outside, then look out and see no one, which is one of the commonest tales associated with the room. Nor did I see the Mad Monk.

The Mad Monk is one of Rowton's best-known ghosts, and he was also my accomplice on the ghost tours. 'My' monk was my good friend Rob. Midway through the ghost tour, I would take the guests up a darkened stairway and into the haunted bedroom. There I would tell them about the ghostly goings-on, and Rob – dressed in a monk's brown robe and cowl –

would come into the room behind them, scream and dash away. Once the laughter had subsided, I would lead the party up another flight of stairs to the top corridor – and that was where my 'encounter' took place. On the night it happened, I assembled the group in the corridor as usual and began to tell another ghost story. It was completely dark, except for the lantern I carried, and so quiet, I could hear people breathing. But suddenly there came a distinct rapping on the corridor ceiling, directly over my head.

I paused and glanced up; there was nothing I could see. I continued my tale. The rapping came again – quite clearly and deliberately, like someone knocking their knuckles against a door. Again, I stopped and looked up. Listened for any sound of movement overhead. Nothing.

By now, the guests were shifting nervously, but smiling. They were assuming it was Rob, adding spooky sound effects from the room above. But I knew two things. Firstly, there were no rooms above us. It was the top corridor; above my head was nothing but roof space. And secondly, Rob was *below* us, on the middle corridor, lying beneath a dresser, preparing to grab unsuspecting ankles in five minutes' time.

I smiled, raised an eyebrow and continued. The rapping came a third time. I took a deep breath, finished the tale and led the guests away.

So that's it. My one and only encounter with something 'strange'. I hope it remains my only one! I am very happy to have a head full of ghosts, but I don't want them following me home . . .

HAUNTED HOUSES

VICTOR SPINETTI – The Vienne Vampire

Victor Spinetti was just about the first person to give us a story for this book. Victor died in 2012 but he had been so helpful and supportive that we are determined to use his strange tale to help raise money for the charity in the way that he intended.

Victor was born in Cwm, Ebbw Vale. He became particularly well known for his roles in all of the Beatles films. Before then he had enjoyed many of his stage successes when working with the celebrated theatre director Joan Littlewood at the Theatre Royal in Stratford, East London. By the late 1970s Joan had moved to live in France and it was on a visit to see her that the following incident occurred.

Victor was staying in Vienne, a town on the river Rhone about 20 miles south of Lyon. He had booked into a hotel, a character-filled building in the oldest part of town close to the cathedral. He was allocated Room 7, which was up on the third floor at the top of a spiral stone staircase.

Inside the room, the bed was situated half within an alcove, so that the head of the bed was partially enclosed and the foot of the bed protruded out into the room. Victor went to bed but during the night found this arrangement rather warm and a bit claustrophobic. To remedy the situation he thought that he might reverse his position in the bed so that

Vienne – La Cathedrale Saint-Maurice. Vienne has many important religious buildings dating from the Norman period and beyond such as the famous gothic Cathedral of St Maurice.

his legs would be in the alcove, rather than the top half of his body, and his head would be in the open part of the room.

As Victor got out of bed and picked up the pillow to move it to the other end of the bed he became aware of what seemed to be a small blue light, almost like a flame, which was glowing in the corner of the bedroom. As he watched the flame it appeared to slowly grow in strength and brightness, until in just a few seconds it was as bright as the flame of a Bunsen burner, and still it seemed to increase in size.

Victor was transfixed by what he was witnessing. Then he saw, as he stared at the flame, what appeared to be the features of a man slowly emerging. The flame then seemed to change again, now transforming itself entirely into the face of a man. The apparition appeared to be grey-haired and with deep, staring, hooded eyes. Unable to move, he still continued to watch as the apparition now started to approach him. It moved slowly closer until eventually it hovered just inches from his own face. Worse still, the apparition omitted a terrible, sickening noise like a gasp as it now started to manoeuvre itself as if it were going to bite his neck.

Throughout all of these happenings Victor had been frozen to the spot with fear, but now, sensing that he was in real danger, he managed to struggle away from the apparition and desperately fumbled with the lights, which were on the outside of the alcove at the head of the bed. As the room was flooded with light the face instantly disappeared. Victor had to get out; he knew that the form would return if he were to attempt to stay the night in the room. Not sure what to do, but not wanting to wake the rest of his group who were in a downstairs room, he quickly dressed and went to the hotel reception, which was deserted. Unlocking the front door, he fled the hotel.

Outside in the dark and ancient town Victor collected his thoughts and finally made himself as comfortable as he could on one of the benches close to the old cathedral. After what he had witnessed in the room he was only able to sleep fitfully and finally he just sat in silence until at last the sun rose.

It was still early in the morning when Victor made his way back to the hotel. He was not keen to return to his room and he started to chat with some of the 'plongeurs', the ladies from the hotel who were busy preparing for breakfast. One of the women remarked that he had risen early. Victor pointed out that, far from being up early, he hadn't in fact been to bed and, what was more, his room was haunted. Victor started to relate his experience in Room 7, but he didn't have to get far into the story before the women confirmed that this was not the first time that visitors had experienced a strange encounter in that particular room. The ladies explained that at one time the hotel had been part of the cathedral buildings and that there was a local legend that this apparition was in fact the spirit of a deranged priest who, in life, had attacked and even murdered his victims.

The rest of the stay at the hotel passed without incident. Victor saw no more of the hotel's ghost and the following evening there was to be no recurrence of the incident of the first night. Victor had taken no chances and, as soon as the reception staff were on duty, he had made arrangements to switch to a different bedroom on another floor of the hotel. One night in Room 7 had been enough for him.

MATT TEBBUTT – The Foxhunter

Matt Tebbutt and his wife Lisa run The Foxhunter, which is a restaurant set in a beautiful area of South Wales, between Abergavenny and Usk. As well as heading up the team in The Foxhunter kitchens, Matt represented Wales on BBC2's Great British Menu in 2007. He is well known as a regular on many cookery programmes.

The Foxhunter is a Grade II listed building and is part of what were once the railway buildings belonging to Nantyderry station. Subsequent to the closure of the station the old stationmaster's house was converted into tea-rooms and more recently a pub. The Foxhunter is actually named after the horse ridden by Nantyderry local, Sir Harry Llewellyn in the 1952 Helsinki Olympic Games. Foxhunter won the only British gold medal of the games and the pub was duly re-named in his honour. Of course Sir Harry Llewellyn was also the Father of Sir Roddy Llewellyn, whose own story also appears in this book.

More recently, The Foxhunter has been completely renovated and original features such as Welsh flagstone floors and log-burning stoves reintroduced. It is the area that was

*The Foxhunter - Originally built to be railway stationmaster's house and
although trains do still use the line nearby, Nantyderry station itself closed at the
end of the 1950's.*

the old bar where this particular incident occurred. Matt told
us that when his daughter was still a toddler she kept pointing
to a corner of The Foxhunter, saying:

'The man, the man!'

But on none of these occasions was there ever anyone there.
While the apparition inspired no fear, she was convinced that
she had seen something. It could be that this was an example
of the particular sensitivities that children can have to
paranormal activity; certainly it was intriguing enough for
Matt to investigate further.

It is interesting that the lingering spirit at The Foxhunter, if that is indeed what it is, does not date from the hundred years when The Foxhunter was being used as a railway property but rather from a time when it was already being used as a pub. The ghost had been conforming more with the current layout and function of the building rather than its earlier railway origins. This was confirmed when Matt and Lisa told us:

'We later found out that apparently a chap did drop dead there about 20 years ago while having a pint and it was confirmed as the exact spot where he was sitting at the bar.'

There have been no more recent sightings of the phantom drinker and we can only conclude that he has now moved on.

MAVIS NICHOLSON – House Hunting in Wales

Mavis presented Thames Television's daily Good Afternoon programmes. Many more series followed including Mavis on 4, on Channel 4. She has worked as the agony aunt for The Oldie Magazine and she edits a community paper in mid-Wales. Mavis has written three books, including a memoir of her childhood in South Wales. This is her story.

My husband and I were thinking of making a gradual move out of London. He was away for a month covering the Tours de France so my sister and I thought that we would do some preliminary house hunting in mid-Wales. We stayed in a small and cosy country hotel. Well, it was nearly very cosy except that the landlord, a gloomy-looking man, was mean with his heating.

He had told us that a house that he knew was up for sale and not yet on the market. I was already pretty sure that I had found something very good: a rather quirky but run-down small farmhouse with a barn in a fantastic setting that I felt my husband and I would be very happy with. But my sister said she felt it in her waters that there was something better just around the corner.

'The spirits are telling you, are they?' I teased her.

'Yes', she said. 'If you must know, they are. I know you do not believe in a spiritual world. But I have proof of such things.'

Almost immediately and there was a rosy-cheeked lady wiping her hands
in her pinafore…..' Copyright © Image courtesy of Harry Nicholson

'Don't start now,' I said as we arrived at the wooden gates of the house we were going to look at. 'Let's agree to differ!'

It was a dishevelled drive, which I liked. The sort of drive that if you see it in a film you know something is going to happen at the end of it. On either side, there were some low-hanging tree branches with the sun slanting through; bluebells like a haze had floated up underneath the trees. There was a lonely, neglected, forlorn feeling about the place that gave you the slightest of shivers. But also it had a definite charm of its own.

The house was a simple double-fronted farmhouse – the kind you draw when you first were asked by teacher to draw a house. We lifted the brass knocker, and it banged with great effect, for the door opened almost immediately and there was a rosy-cheeked lady wiping her hands in her pinafore.

'Hello, you've come to see my house,' she greeted us.

'We have,' I said, shaking her hand, 'and this is my sister who has come with me.'

'Like a cuppa? Or would you rather see round first?'

'See round first,' we both answered.

It was a gem. The oak beams had all been kept in their natural state – no heavy black stain on them. Huge slate slabs on the floors. The kitchen had a beautiful old Welsh dresser. The pantry had slate slabs and was sunless and icy cold and the owner had her labelled pickles and jams very appetisingly arrayed on scrubbed shelves.

A dear little oak stairs took us upstairs to two of the bedrooms, which were light and a very decent size, but when we walked into the third one I shivered. It was out of the sun and rather dark. My sister took one step in and spun round on her heel and stayed outside.

We followed the woman downstairs into the kitchen, where the kettle had boiled, and she made us a cup of tea. As she handed one to my sister, she said, 'You felt it then?'

'I did,' said my sister, who was still looking chilled by her experience.

Oh, help! I thought, we are now well and truly into ghosts!

'That was not a pleasant experience exactly,' my sister said.

'It never is,' said the owner. 'The daughter of the house hanged herself in that room. My husband never felt anything,' said our hostess, 'but I have. I felt the spirit was antagonistic and very angry. In fact I had a spiritualist come and try to put the spirit to rest, but it was not possible. And then everything seemed to calm down. My husband very much liked the room and used it as his study. He actually died in it some fourteen years ago. I can't manage here any more, which is the only reason I want to move. For it is a lovely setting and we have never changed the old house. It is as it always has been.

'I am sure that the spirit won't affect you at all,' she said, turning to me; and I thought she looked a bit impatiently at me.

I was ready to leave. But my sister and the owner wanted to relate other experiences they'd had, including objects that had moved in their rooms by some spiritual force . . .

We left eventually and I said I would be in touch. Though I knew this house was not for me, somehow. As we walked down the drive I glanced back and there was the woman at her front door and a tall, young girl standing like a shadow just behind her . . . I did not mention it to my sister as she would say, 'See, I told you so!'

And I was still positive there was a simple explanation for the presence! Like the owner had a daughter who had been out in the garden while we looked around and she had returned. . . . Unless, of course, my sister and the owner were on to something that I did not believe in!

When we got back from the hotel we popped into the bar for a drink before we set off back home. The landlord was there and asked us if we had liked the look of the house.

'Yes, indeed,' I said. 'And the owner showed us round . . .'
He interrupted: 'No, you couldn't have met the owner,' he said. 'She died about a month ago.'

'Bloody Hell!' exclaimed my sister.

I explained to him again that a woman had shown us round who said she was the owner.

'Well, I cannot for the life of me understand this. It must have been a cleaner hired by the estate agent or something like that,' mine host stated firmly.

I was more than willing to go along with that. My sister was not.

She positively bloomed on the journey home. Saying that there was more to life and death than anyone could comprehend. People ought to leave their minds open to experience whatever life threw up and not to have hard and fast theories, especially when those same people had no proof and were too frightened to seek it. They were foolish to have closed their minds and hearts to the glory and mystery of life and death. Wow! She was having them and getting at me in a big way!

And she had sort of won the day.

And I am left steadfastly floundering!

SOPHIE EVANS – Pugh's Farm

Sophie came to prominence on the Television show Over the Rainbow. She appeared as Dorothy in The Wizard of Oz at the London Palladium and now regularly appears on stage and the television. Sophie was born and raised in the Rhondda Valley and her story comes from her childhood.

After coming home from school, my younger sister and I decided to take the dog for a walk. My father also came along with us as I was 11 and my sister was 8 years old.

We decided to walk to a place called 'Pugh's Farm', which is situated on the mountain about a mile from where we lived.

Pugh's Farm in about 1900. Now demolished and the land built on.
Copyright © Image courtesy of Rhondda Cynon Taf libraries

The farmhouse was a ruin, but everybody knew exactly where it was.

It was a lovely clear day, although a little cold. The dog was bounding through the uneven ground around him, and we were all having a lovely time. My father said, 'Girls, turn around and I'll take a picture of you in front of the ruins.' It hadn't been long since Christmas, when my sister and me were given a new camera as a present, so we were using it at every opportunity. It was an instant camera where as soon as you took the picture, you'd wait a few seconds and pull out your snapshot. So we both turned to the camera with our arms in the air pointing at the ruin, as if we were models for it.

A few seconds later the photo was developed, and to our amazement there was something a little extra on our photo. Where we had been pointing at the farmhouse a figure had appeared: a head, shoulders, body and feet, which was bright gold.

We were all amazed and we couldn't wait to run home and show our mother. We had the picture made bigger to get a better look at it; it now hangs in the kitchen and we always say that the figure is our guardian angel!

But, maybe, the strangest thing of all is that about ten years ago the ruin was knocked down and new houses were built there. Soon after my family and I moved into one of the new houses, and as we unpacked our boxes to move in, we unpacked our photo, and my mother said to my father, 'Do you know exactly where this photo would have been taken?'

He looked at my mother and paused for a while, thinking, then he said, 'Yes I do; I would say it was exactly where this house is!'

We all gasped, and thought how strange, but it was a nice strange feeling; we like to think we were guided here by our guardian angel . . .

Well, we like to think that anyway.

ANDY SECOMBE – The Lady of Whitehall

Andy Secombe was born in The Mumbles. He is an actor and an author. As well as fantasy novels he has published a further book of memories and reflections on his own childhood: Growing up with the Goons. Andy's story comes from this earlier time.

When I was growing up, the family home was near Cheam Village, in Surrey. Cheam had the distinction of being the original location of Cheam School, which Prince Philip attended in his boyhood. The school has since moved to Berkshire, but it was originally housed in a building called 'Whitehall'.

When I was living in Cheam, I would often pass Whitehall and marvel at its antiquity. I was fascinated by the idea that this perfectly preserved timber building provided a link back to the times of Henry VIII. It wasn't just historical, it *was* history, and to look at it, or even better, to touch it, was to feel

Whitehall with bus passing. The haunted window is in the centre.

the thrill of having a channel back in time – like Tony and Doug in the sixties sci-fi television series, *The Time Tunnel*.

One day, when I was about twelve years old, I took the bus home to North Cheam which, as its name suggests, was then, and unless the geography of Greater London has recently been affected by a massive movement of the tectonic plates, still is a couple of miles north of Cheam Village. I was the drummer in a school band and North Cheam was the location of the best drum shop in the area, so, most Saturdays, I would take the bus there to drool over the racks of glittering Paiste cymbals and gleaming Ludwig drum kits in the latest 'pearl sparkle' style. The bus passed Whitehall and as I always travelled on the top deck, I was able to stare into the upstairs window of the projecting room above the porch, which I would people in my imagination with, depending on my mood, grand lords and ladies or bootblacks and buxom serving wenches.

In reality, the room beyond the window in the Tudor house was always empty, dark and featureless, but this one particular autumn day I was surprised to see it occupied. Sitting at a dressing table, set with two large silver candelabra, a lady, perhaps in her mid-fifties and dressed in a simple white nightgown, was stroking a silver-backed brush through her long white hair. As the bus passed by, she looked up and for a moment our eyes met. She seemed as startled as me, for her eyes widened in shock, but almost immediately I was once more staring at the neat red bricks of fifties and sixties domestic architecture on Malden Road, as the bus moved on.

At the time I remember thinking it strange, as I had no idea that anyone lived there. I resolved to ask my sister, Jennifer, who went to Nonsuch Grammar School and had recently done a project on the history of the village, if she knew who occupied the house. But after the excitement of the drum shop and the purchase of a new set of nylon-tipped drumsticks, 'just in from America', I forgot all about it.

It was perhaps a week later when I finally remembered the Whitehall incident and quizzed my sister about the old lady who lived in the house.

'No one lives there now,' she replied. 'The place has been empty for years. I think the council has just bought it and is planning to turn it into a museum.' A small shiver trickled down my spine as I remembered what I had seen.

There are some who believe that time is an illusion; that past, present and future occur simultaneously and that certain people, in the right frame of mind, can rise above the 'now' and observe events from both the past and the future. Perhaps my old lady was a ghost – I certainly don't rule out the possibility that spirits or 'energies' can linger around certain places or buildings – but what I saw that day was so real, the woman so solidly corporeal, that the experience left me with the conviction that what I had seen wasn't a spectre, but that I had rather peeped through a chink in time to witness a very private moment in some long-dead person's life. And perhaps she had peered back at me and despaired to see a future that promised nothing but drum-mad adolescent boys.

EDWARD MARSTON – The Phantom Coach and The Grey Lady

Edward Marston has written over forty original plays for radio, television and the theatre. He now concentrates on developing the various series of crime novels that he has worked on over the years (such as the Restoration series, the Railway Detective series and the Captain Daniel Rawson series). Edward was born and brought up in South Wales, and this is his story.

When I graduated from Oxford, I moved to the Midlands and played rugby for a team of Welsh exiles in Birmingham.

Corley Hall. Here seen well over a hundred years ago. It was believed to be the model for Hall Farm in George Eliot's novel, Adam Bede.
© Image courtesy of Coventry History Centre

I didn't realise at the time that one of the men I played against twice a year would become a close friend and fellow ghost hunter. Our first house was half of an old school. Built in 1660, it was full of character. It also had lots of strange noises at night that we chose to ignore. As the children began to grow up, we needed a bigger place and bought a farmhouse in Warwickshire. While waiting to pick up the kids from the village school, I chatted to one of the mothers there and told her that we hoped to defray the cost of the restoration work by doing some of it ourselves. She promptly offered her husband's help.

I was surprised to find that the hulking second row forward I'd met on a rugby field so many times lived quite close by. Trained as a draughtsman, he'd designed a double garage and a kitchen extension at his house then got the plans passed by an architect friend. He'd built everything single-handed. The work was of such a high standard that I took him on at once. Corley Hall, our new home, was a rambling farmhouse with medieval origins. And it was rumoured to have ghosts.

Since the house was in the middle of a dairy farm, we got to know the farmer and his family very well. They were unfailingly helpful, providing all sorts of tackle free of charge. The farmer's wife recounted the story of the phantom coach. She and her family had lived in Corley Hall for many years and had heard tales about a coach that had thundered down the drive once a year. They didn't believe the stories until the night when Meg was innocently sitting in the outside privy. She swore that she suddenly heard the noise of a coach and horses then felt a fierce rush of wind as they swept past. She never used that privy again. We had it taken down and the bricks were incorporated in a garage designed by my brother, a Newport architect.

Bill and I spent three days a week on site, taking out fireplaces, laying new floors, plumbing, plastering, painting and doing all the other jobs needed before we could move in. We tended to discount the story of the phantom coach. Then Bill happened to be putting in a new bath upstairs. It was broad daylight. I was in the living room when I heard this loud yell and Bill pounded down the stairs as if the hounds of hell were on his tail. A man who'd tuck a rugby ball under his arm and run through a brick wall was now gibbering with fear. He'd seen the hazy outline of an old lady move from one bedroom to another. In fact, when I'd been alone downstairs, I often thought I'd heard footsteps above me but put it down to the settlement of ancient timbers.

We searched the two bedrooms but found no trace of anyone. If she was a ghost, she was a benign presence and we christened her the grey lady. A number of guests who slept in the relevant bedrooms claim to have heard footsteps in the night but none of them saw what my friend did. Corley Hall is mentioned in Pevsner's Warwickshire guide and its architectural features are listed. Not a word about the phantom coach or the grey lady, however. But there are at least two people who will take their Bible oath that they had a close encounter with a ghost at the house.

GAOLS

SARA SUGARMAN – Wandsworth Prison

Sara is an actress and film-maker. She was born in Rhyl in North Wales. She has worked as a film director and her films include Disney's Confessions of a Teenage Drama Queen (2004) and Very Annie Mary (2001).

In Sara's 1999 film *Mad Cows* the central character, Maddy, is gaoled for stealing a packet of peas and there is a twenty-minute section shot inside prison, prior to Maddy's escape. Very unusually, when filming *Mad Cows*, Sara and her film crew were allowed to have access to the interior of Wandsworth Prison.

Wandsworth Prison is an old and historic building. It was largely built in the middle of the nineteenth century.

Wandsworth Prison. Wandsworth prison was modelled on Pentonville.
This design involves a series of wings branching off a central rotunda.

Wandsworth became part of the national prison system in 1878 and it was at this point, with the closure of other prisons, that Wandsworth became an execution prison. Interestingly, the condemned cell and execution chamber did still exist until very recently when E Wing was refurbished. Indeed the gallows themselves were kept in working order long after the abolition of the death penalty, in case they were ever needed again.

Sara explained to us how, when she was filming the prison section of *Mad Cows* (with a bunch of supermodels making cameo appearances such as Sophie Dahl and Jodie Kidd) that it had been a really unpleasant day due to the oppressive feel of the prison. Sara described to us in her own words a

further incident which happened during a break in the
filming of the Wandsworth scenes.

*The guard said, 'Come with me', and I followed him into a nondescript
room. He said, 'Stand there.' I stood in the middle of a boring room .
. . A horribly strong sensation came over me. I felt dizzy and really
deeply unhappy. Like a lot of emotional pain but also dizziness. He
said, 'That's where they did the hanging of the prisoners.' It was awful,
I really felt the terror and disturbance before I knew what it was.*

It seems that Sara's experience is not uncommon. In addition
to the feelings caused by the execution chamber, there is
thought to be at least one ghost at the prison and this is the
ghost of a grey lady. This apparition has been spotted on a
number of occasions and is thought to be wearing prison
clothing. Of course Wandsworth is now only a prison for
men, but that was not always so, as up until the 1890s the
prison also accommodated women prisoners. From this we
can assume that the spectral inmate is likely to have come
from the late nineteenth century. There have been 135
executions at the prison, but only one of these has been of a
woman: this was Kate Webster, and it has been suggested
that the ghost may in fact be Kate's spirit.

In life Kate had come from Killane in County Wexford but
was no stranger to Wandsworth Prison. Her final visit, the
one that led to the gallows, followed the murder of her
employer, Julia Thomas in South London. It is thought that
the murder had been committed with a blow from an axe
and then by throwing Julia downstairs. The body was then
dismembered and disposed of. While some parts of the body
were retrieved from the river, the head was not found at the
time. Even without the sophisticated techniques for

identifying the body which we now have, there was little doubt as to what Kate Webster had done. She was tried and executed in the prison.

Perhaps the curiosity of the grey lady had been aroused by the appearance of so many other women attired in prison clothing during the making of Sara's film.

As an interesting postscript to this story, in 2010, after an interval of well over a hundred years, what has now been identified as the head of Julia Thomas has been recovered. It was found during building works in the grounds of a pub, The Hole in the Wall, which had been local to the murder scene. It will be interesting to find out if the sightings of the grey lady cease as a result of this grisly find.

LEE COLLIN BAXTER – Arundel Gaol

Lee Collin Baxter was born in Liverpool but spent his formative years living in Rhiwbina, Cardiff, South Wales. He was a member of the half British, half Dutch boy band Caught in the Act who sold over 15 million singles and albums and won fifteen gold and two platinum albums. He now regularly appears on stage and on the screen under the name of Collin Baxter. In addition to his career as a performer, Collin has run the Arundel Gaol for some years and knows the building as well as anyone.

Arundel Gaol in Sussex was originally built in 1836 as an undercroft to Arundel Town Hall. It served as the gaol for

Arundel in West Sussex with the impressive castle overlooking the town

those prisoners convicted in the courtrooms upstairs. It has been the scene of several notable trials and at least one daring escape.

From 1964 the old gaol served as the town museum, but by the late 1970s that too had moved on to new premises. These days the old gaol is known as The Arundel Jailhouse. A popular venue for local bands, comedy nights, murder mystery dinners, spooky tours, it is also used as a theatre space. Because of the interesting history of the building it has become a popular destination for paranormal groups. They have frequently reported hearing phenomena such as banging doors, slamming sounds and other knocking noises; surely the distant echoes of a working gaol.

Frequently Collin has found himself alone in the gaol late at night when he is locking up. The clanking of the doors and the rattle of the keys as he secures the building are a reminder of the gaol's grim past. On at least one occasion he has experienced pictures falling off walls and electrical equipment switching itself on or off.

In the early days, when Collin had just taken over the running of this unique venue, he would often let his evening staff go home a little earlier than himself while he finished the book keeping, but too many weird occurrences means he keeps at least one member of staff on with him till they're both up the dark stairway and the gate is locked. 'I do feel like a bit of a chicken and I'm sure my mind is probably making things ten times worse than they are but the energy in there does seem to change when you're alone late at night,' says Collin. 'It gets colder and often you can hear knocking coming from the Town Hall above.' This phenomenon has also been reported by several different paranormal groups with some coming back again and again to try and solve this mystery . . . 'What is causing this knocking and where precisely is it coming from? We've checked with the Town Hall and there are no security guards wandering around up there at 2am, so the mystery continues.'

One of his most memorable incidents, though, left one employee a complete wreck, to the point where she quit her job and refuses to even set foot in the Jailhouse! 'It happened at the end of one of our murder mystery evenings and all the customers had left and we were clearing up. This one member of staff, Mandy, was on her own in the kitchen, washing up. I was in the main area stacking the chairs when out of the corner of my eye I saw a flash of light by the entrance to the kitchen and the swing lid of the bin smashed open and shut, as if someone had whacked it with their hand, but there was nobody near it. Then I heard Mandy scream and then all the lights went out for about five seconds. When they came back on, the fire alarm went off. Eventually after everything had calmed down Mandy told me that she too saw the flash of light and the bin and that when the lights went out she felt a presence in the kitchen with her. She was very shaken by the experience. The fact that we both witnessed it leads me to believe that there is more to these events than just tricks of the mind.

THEATRE GHOSTS

Wyn Calvin – Theatre Royal, Drury Lane

Wyn Calvin MBE OStJ was born in Pembrokeshire. He is a past 'King Rat' of the Grand Order of Water Rats (Britain's premier show-business charity) and has appeared at many famous theatres in the British Isles. The following story relates to The Theatre Royal, Drury Lane, one of the most historic theatres in London and, it seems, one of the most haunted. The most regularly seen ghost is that of a man in grey, who is said to be a nobleman in eighteenth-century costume.

The Impressive frontage of The Theatre Royal Drury Lane.
The theatre has always been famous for its lavish productions including spectacular events such as battles or chariot races.

Walter MacQueen-Pope was in charge of publicity at the Theatre Royal, Drury Lane for twenty-one years and from 1720 there was always a member of his family connected to the theatre. He was a prolific writer of books about the theatre and his role in the story will become apparent in a moment.

The following account is in Wyn's own words.

It was 1945 and I had my first job as a juvenile in a revue for ENSA, the wartime entertainment for HM Forces. The headquarters of its operations was the Theatre Royal, Drury Lane in London.

As a very young performer rehearsing in the Theatre Royal (a 'teenager' before the expression came into common use), I was thrilled to be in one of the world's most famous theatres. One afternoon, while wandering in awe – and semi-darkness – at the side of the empty dress circle to absorb the atmosphere I caught a glimpse of a character in Restoration costume on the other side of the dress circle. Curious to know what period play was being rehearsed within the theatre (for here was obviously an actor trying out his costume) I was sorry that, when I crossed at the back of the circle to approach him, he had disappeared.

Later, in the canteen, I asked what period play was being cast in one of the theatre's rehearsal rooms, describing the cloak, hat and costume I'd seen. At another table a man asked me to repeat what I had said. Nervous now, as a very inexperienced youth I thought maybe I could be getting someone into trouble for walking about in costume. He insisted, however, and I nervously described the figure seen in semi-darkness that afternoon.

The gentleman said, 'Come with me and speak to someone who will be interested.' Still fearing my possible indiscretion I was taken to the door marked *W. MacQueen-Pope, Press Officer* and told to tell Mr MacQueen-Pope what I had seen. The distinguished theatre historian listened with special interest and then said, 'Young man, you have just seen a ghost.'

Thinking that it was now some leg-pull or tease of an obviously uncouth youth, I said, 'But it was this afternoon; you only get ghosts at night.'

Smiling, the gentleman continued: 'He has always been seen during the day; even during packed matinees he appears to have joined the crowd to watch a performance. Now I am going to ask you to sign a book which contains the signatures of others, over many years, who have experienced what you have seen today.'

You may now ask me if I believe in ghosts. I can only reply with certainty, 'I don't know.'

SEBASTIAN HARCOMBE – The Fortune Theatre

Sebastian Harcombe was born in the Rhondda Valley, South Wales and has worked extensively as an actor, including at both the Royal National Theatre and the Royal Shakespeare Company, but it was while appearing in The Woman in Black in the West End back in 2002 that he had his own memorable ghostly encounter.

For anyone who doesn't know, the story of *The Woman in Black* involves ghostly events taking place in and around a solitary house set on the salt marshes. In the first half of the play there is a scene set in a graveyard. It is at this point that a ghostly apparition makes a startling appearance and the protagonists and audience get an early glimpse of the ghostly Woman in Black. While Sebastian was on stage, in the build-up to the appearance of the Woman in Black, he looked up into the wings and distinctly saw two figures waiting to make their entrance, rather than the one that he had been

The Fortune Theatre. One of the smallest of the West End theatres, built in the 1920's and home to 'The Woman in Black' since the mid 1980's.

expecting; both were similarly attired in black. At the appropriate moment a few seconds later, the actress continued onto the stage alone, leaving the second woman standing in the wings. By the end of the scene the second figure was no longer there.

Sebastian had been shaken by what he had seen, but thought that there must be a rational explanation. For example, he thought that perhaps it was one of the stage management team playing a trick on the actors. During the interval, it was discovered that the Assistant Stage Manager was actually stage left at that point in the show and nowhere near where the ghostly sighting had occurred. To compound the spooky experience, the leading lady mentioned that while she had not actually seen anything, she had felt that she had been followed onto the stage by someone that she couldn't see.

The spooky encounters were not restricted to that one performance. At around the same time as Sebastian's experience a further female figure was seen to appear on several occasions in one of the lower boxes of the theatre. One account suggests that these spooky visions came after there was a break-in at the theatre, and it is believed that the ghost has come to protect the theatre and keep an eye on everything that has been going on.

CONNIE FISHER – The London Palladium

Connie Fisher was brought up in Pembrokeshire, and first came to prominence by winning the BBC show, How Do You Solve A Problem Like Maria? Since then she has regularly been seen on the stage and screen. Connie's spooky story relates to probably the most famous theatre in the United Kingdom, the London Palladium.

Opening a show at the London Palladium in 2006 was an exciting time for me, and admittedly my head was in the clouds for quite some time after I won the part of Maria. After the dust had settled and we were enjoying our run at London's most prolific theatre, my dresser, Lyn, who was responsible for dressing me during the show and who often

The London Palladium

made us cups of tea in the interval, noticed something spooky start to happen in my dressing room.

As Lyn was responsible for dressing me during the show she spent more time than anyone in the 'Gracie Fields' dressing room. I remember Lyn was quite superstitious about the theatre, and one day I happened to whistle in my dressing room, so she made me leave the room, spin round three times and spit on the floor outside – not something I'm in the habit of doing, but something you're supposed to do, according to superstition, to avoid something bad happening. So after that I teased Lyn a lot about the ghost of Gracie Fields haunting my room. I played a few jokes, jumped out from behind my rail of costumes, that kind of thing, and in response she would tell me many ghost stories from her time and experience in other theatres, to try to convince me that ghosts were real. I remember one story in particular, when she worked in Drury Lane and saw a woman in a black dress walk straight through a wall!

Before the show Lyn would always make me a cup of honey and lemon, in a cup and saucer that she bought me, as she would be the first in the dressing room and often the one who locked up. One evening I came into work and Lyn asked me if I had decided to make my own honey and lemon that night, and I responded that I had only just got in and hadn't had a drink yet. I thought nothing of this conversation, until the next night, when she asked again whether I had made myself a cuppa and did I want another one? Yet again I responded that I'd only just got in and hadn't made myself a drink yet.

The next day she asked me again and I was so confused I asked her why every night she thought I had been making myself a drink . . . without saying anything she showed me the cup and saucer that I drank out of every night, and it was placed upside down, and the rim was so heavily smeared in honey that it was stuck to the saucer. It had obviously been there some time as the honey had hardened and gone tacky, so the cup was hard to remove. It wasn't the way anyone would leave a cup and saucer after they had drunk out of it, and we always washed up every night before we left and the room was locked until we came in the following day. So how the cup ended up upside down covered in honey I shall never know, but we put it down to a dressing room haunting and affectionately called our visiting ghost the 'honey monster', and it continued to happen for about two weeks.

Then one day Lyn and I held a bit of a vigil and asked the honey monster, out loud, to please stop playing tricks on us (we must have sounded like right lunatics) but from that day forward it never happened again . . .

It could well have been the night watchman having a laugh, but something tells me, in a place like the London Palladium, with all its ghostly history, it was probably something from the other side . . .

PERSONAL PHENOMENA

PHIL CARRADICE – An Assessment Centre in Essex

Phil Carradice is a poet, novelist and short story writer, and is also the host of the BBC Radio Wales series The Past Master. Phil was born in Pembroke Dock and originally worked in the fields of teaching and social work, and his tale comes from that period in his life.

A long time ago, soon after I had begun teaching, I went to work in what was then called an Assessment Centre in Essex. It was my first time out of Wales and whether or not that had any bearing on the events of that night – homesickness and the like – I leave it for you to decide.

The work was hard and gruelling, with boys who had committed serious crimes: murder, armed robbery and the like. And so the need to 'let off steam' now and again was, I guess, fairly natural. One Saturday night we had a party in the house of one member of staff. It was the usual thing: lots of drinking, shouting and fooling around. But late that night when virtually everyone else had staggered off to bed, my wife and I sat with one or two of the last revellers. Included in them was Norman.

Norman had just come to work in the Centre and so we didn't know a lot about him. But we did know that he attended a spiritualist church in the town. We didn't think anything more about it – it was something he did in his free time.

Suddenly Norman sat up, put down his drink and stared at Judy, my wife. 'There's somebody here wants to talk with you, wants to let you know he's all right,' he said. We looked around in alarm and then, with laughter bubbling under the surface, we stared at him. We didn't believe, we were sceptical, but for some reason – perhaps it was something in Norman's voice – we didn't mock. 'Go on,' said Judy.

It was simple enough. This tall, dark man wanted to let her know he was all right and, more importantly, she should contact her mother – she had been unwell. 'Who is this man?' asked my wife. Norman described him, right down to a chip in his front tooth. Apart from the chip it sounded exactly like Judy's father, who had died just a few months before. 'He's perfectly happy,' said Norman. 'He wants you to know that. But you must ring your mother.'
We went home and the following morning Judy telephoned her mother. She had, indeed, been unwell but was feeling better now – the phone call helped and we arranged for her to come up from Wales on a visit. 'Dad didn't have a chip on his front tooth, did he?' Judy asked at the end of the conversation.

Her mother was amazed. 'How did you know? The day before he died he dropped his false teeth and chipped them. Nobody ever knew, not you, your sisters, nobody.'

I watched Judy's eyes widening as she listened to her mother. She was clearly astounded and perhaps a little afraid. She had never been told about the chip in the teeth and she had certainly never seen it. So how on earth could Norman, a man she had never met before that night, possibly know? I felt a cold shiver up my back when she put down the phone and told me the story. It's still there, even now, whenever I think of that night. And I'm still left with the question – how on earth did Norman know?

COLIN R. PARSONS – Chills on a Knife Edge

Colin is a popular sci-fi and fantasy author. He was born in the Rhondda Valley and still lives in Wales. It was here that his strange incident occurred . . .

We got married in 1985 and one of our wedding presents was an electric carving knife. It was proudly given to us by my Uncle Emlyn. Like I said, this was the mid-eighties and an electric knife was a 'must have' item at the time. None of our friends had one and I couldn't thank my dear old uncle enough.

Sadly, he died a few years later. I was left empty at my loss and so was my wife, who loved him too. We kept using the knife and it was a warm reminder of his presence. But this wasn't going to be the end of my connection with him.

One evening, after a particularly strenuous day, my wife made dinner, which included a small joint of beef. So, I carved nice, even, juicy slices, as our knife happily buzzed through the tender meat. We ate our meal and settled down on the sofa for a relaxing evening watching telly. The dishes, I told my wife, I would do later (fully intending not to do them until the morning).

We were halfway through an episode of our favourite Australian soap, *Neighbours*, when I heard something buzzing in the kitchen, then it stopped. I dismissed the thought of it being the knife as absurd. I put it down to, maybe, being the fridge freezer kicking in or something. My wife glanced at me and I just shook my head and smiled. We carried on watching the show. But to our distress, it happened again, a continuous buzzing sound in the kitchen. We peered into one another's eyes with scepticism; this time, though, the noise didn't stop!

We got up off the settee and gingerly made our way to the kitchen, filled with dread. When we entered, we saw, to our utter horror, the electric knife working on its own, its steel blades vibrating at a furious rate. My mouth was dry and my wife was physically shaking.

'I-it's probably just an electric surge,' I said in a stutter, as the knife was still plugged into the point. 'Needs a service, I expect,' I added, and nervously reached out and jabbed at the switch. To our relief it stopped immediately when it was turned off.

'Thank God for that,' my wife exclaimed. All done and explained, we went back into the living room and made ourselves comfortable again. There was no Sky+ back then, so we missed whatever was playing out while we were obviously preoccupied in the kitchen. Jan flicked the channel over and a cooking programme had already started. The chef was about to carve a joint.

'They could've used our knife to cut that meat,' I joked with a nervous smirk but, to my dismay, the buzzing sound erupted once more. This time we were terrified. Janice refused to go out there and I didn't want to go either but, being the 'man of the house,' I had no choice.

I trembled as I edged my way back to the kitchen. When I entered, I stood speechless and petrified. There on the worktop was our electric knife, vibrating away on the surface, with no electricity to power it, but somehow it was still working!

My heart thumped in my chest and I could hardly swallow. The knife then stopped as abruptly as it had started. I seized my chance. Swiftly, I grasped the handle and simultaneously flipped open the metal pedal bin. Trembling and almost not able to breathe, I pressed the button to release the blades and let them slip inside. The lid came down with a clang. I took the body of the knife outside and smashed it into little bits with a hammer. I threw all the broken pieces into the bin . . . and we've never spoken about the incident since until writing this story.

DAFYDD IWAN – A Strange Night at Glan-llyn

Dafydd Iwan is a Welsh singer and politician and, for a long time, was the President of Plaid Cymru. As a songwriter he composed 'Yma o Hyd', one of the great patriotic songs of Wales. This is Dafydd's contribution.

I was living at the time in Llanuwchllyn, a village the other end of the lake from Bala, and between the two places, overlooking Llyn Tegid, was Glan-llyn, the Urdd camp for older teenagers. My brother Huw and I used to work in the kitchen at the camp, but spent much of our time there even when we were not working. In the evenings, I used to sing a few songs and Huw took part in the sketches to keep the campers entertained.

One evening, a group of us ventured into the cellar (or 'dungeon' as we used to call it, to whet the curiosity of the younger campers) where we sometimes held story-telling sessions. Due to the rather eerie nature of the cellar, and especially the reddish-brown stain running down one wall – which, according to many generations of Glan-llyn folklore, was the bloodstain following the gruesome murder of the daughter of the *plas* owner – the stories told there were often of ghosts and various forms of supernatural events.

I didn't 'believe' in ghosts, and neither did anyone else present as far as I knew, but we were all drawn by the strange forces which we have all experienced at one time or another to that twilight world where unexplained things happen. Or at least the world of stories about unexplained things which hint at a dimension beyond this life of ours. And there, in

Llanuwchllyn station is the terminus of the Bala Lake railway. It's famous for its scenic views but Dafydd's story shows a more mysterious side to the area.

the dark dungeon below the old *plasdy* of Glan-llyn, lit only by the flickering flame of the storm-lamp which cast tall shadows on the blood-stained wall, we heard stories – many of which we had heard before – about ancient murders, howling wolves and ghostly figures disappearing through stone walls.

The stories soon led to someone suggesting a 'Ouija' session, where letters were marked in a circle on a table, and an inverted tumbler was placed in the centre. I had never been in one of these sessions before, but I had heard stories about them, and clearly one or two in the party were very apprehensive about taking part and dropped out. But even they could not drag themselves away, and stayed to watch. The rest of us placed a hand lightly on the tumbler, and one of the party began to ask questions of the 'spirit', beginning with fairly innocuous ones about birthdays and suchlike.

But I remember the session for one reason: when asked if the 'spirit' had anything in particular to say to us, the tumbler kept going in the direction of the three letters S, B and J. When asked to elaborate, these three letters kept being repeated, time and time again. We soon became bored, the atmosphere began to disintegrate, and we decided to call it a day, and return to more earthly things.

Huw and I decided it was high time we began the long trek home, so we bade our farewells, and left in the direction of Llanuwchllyn. It was a fine night, but alternating between heavy cloud-cover and bursts of bright moonlight. As we walked along the road to the village, we kept to the white line in the middle of the road because when the clouds came it became very dark. My brother suddenly asked me if I could hear something, and I told him that I felt someone was walking behind us, some distance away. We walked on, and the footsteps behind us came closer, and we could feel our own footsteps quickening. I couldn't resist the temptation, and turned round, but as I did so, the clouds closed and I couldn't see a thing, but there was someone there. My brother looked as well and whispered to me that he thought he saw three or four people walking in a line. By now we were almost running, with sweat running down my back. Suddenly, we stopped; the footsteps had gone, the clouds broke, and in the clear moonlight we could see that the road was empty.

We hastened home, both of us by now in a strangely disturbed frame of mind. It was well past two in the morning by the time we got to Garth Gwyn, and we entered as quietly as we could, for fear of Dad's wrath, and took our shoes off at the front door. We entered the kitchen to get a glass of water before going upstairs, and Dad had left us a note on the kitchen table. It was a message of one simple sentence: 'Mae Ewyrth Seimon wedi marw.' (My father's uncle, the Reverend Simon B. Jones, was a pacifist preacher and poet who had won both the Crown and Chair at the National Eisteddfod, and he had died that night.)

Postscript:

We heard some time later that there had been army manoeuvres in the area that week, which probably accounts for the mysterious figures in the road, and they would have left us to go cross-country in the direction of Trawsfynydd. But to this day it is highly improbable that the news of Simon B. Jones' death had reached Glan-llyn, and even if it had, I doubt whether anyone in that 'Ouija' party would have played such an insensitive trick on us. It remains therefore one of those 'unexplained' secrets, which only comes to light at times like these. As another Welsh poet, T.H. Parry-Williams, once said of fairies when asked if he 'believed' in them: 'No, I don't believe in them, but they do exist.'

SAM STONE – The Boxes

Sam is an award-winning author, well known for her horror and fantasy books, particularly the Vampire Gene series. She has lived in North Wales but her story relates to her childhood in Manchester.

When I was a little girl I used to really enjoy staying up late to watch Hammer Horror movies on television with my sister. We used to bring our duvets and pillows downstairs and lie on our stomachs on the floor in front of the television. There were midnight snacks: Dandelion and Burdock fizzy drinks with bags of crisps and chocolate. This was all fun until the day my mother brought home the boxes.

My mum loved brass. She collected all manner of ornaments and plates, bells and horseshoes, but this one day she brought into the house two wooden boxes that had brass panels attached on one side. One panel showed a picture of a coach and horses; the other was of some children playing. On the top of each box was a cushioned lid. The fabric was pale pink velvet that looked tired and worn. I noticed that the wood was very old. The boxes had a peculiar smell and my imagination filled in the blanks as to what these had previously been used for. The wood reminded me of smoothed shipwreck wood and the smell was slightly salty and reminiscent of the sea. The boxes looked like treasure chests.

'These will make great toy boxes,' she said. And we proceeded to fill them with all sorts of dolls and teddies. Mum put the chests either side of the gas fireplace and they rapidly became part of the modern fixtures and fittings of our home.

On the following weekend, my sister and I stayed up to catch the latest horror movies. Sometimes when we did this, we fell asleep downstairs before the films had finished and this was one such night. I curled up on one of the sofas and let my eyes close. The room was in darkness but for the gas fire, which was lit and filled the room with a warm glow. I don't remember when the film finished, or when my sister turned off the TV, but I recall waking sometime in the night and I found myself staring at the fire.

I was half asleep and it took me a while to realise that the room looked different, and the boring gas fire had been replaced by a huge fireplace: a fire burned there.

I blinked. I felt awake now and I looked around the room, only to realise that this was not the room I fell asleep in. I found myself looking in on what appeared to be a small drama. I saw a young woman; her hair was swept back from her face at the front, but fell down over her back and shoulders. She was wearing unusual clothing. Old fashioned. Thinking back I realise that she was dressed in something that might have been eighteenth century but I'm not really sure. She was sitting on top of the box to the left of the fire and I realised that this was one of the chests that my mother had brought home. At her feet was a baby. I can't recall whether it was a little boy or girl, I just remember it was young enough to only be able to crawl.

I was convinced I was dreaming until the woman, who had been looking down at the child, turned and looked directly at me. I fell back against the arm of the sofa then. I felt scared, but not terrified, and then the woman's face seemed to evaporate and I was left with the impression of just her eyes floating before me.

I think I blacked out then. Or maybe I woke up for real – I've never really been sure. But for a long time as I was growing up I truly believed I had seen the woman and the baby and I felt that they were somehow associated with those unusual chests.

I'm not sure what happened to the boxes. They vanished over time, perhaps resold by my parents when times were hard and money was needed. Maybe they were haunted. Maybe it was just my teenage imagination stimulated by the horror movies that made the whole incident so vivid to me. But one thing I know for sure. I wasn't dreaming.

I have never forgotten my experience. Maybe I was seeing the ghost of some woman, or perhaps, just perhaps, she was seeing an echo of me watching her from the future.

THE GREAT WELSH OUTDOORS

HUW STEPHENS – Bardsey Island

Huw Stephens is a regular presenter on BBC Radio 1. He was born in Cardiff and is well known for his passion for discovering and championing new music. Huw's choice of spooky location for us can be found just off the coast of north-west Wales.

One of the most beautiful places in Wales is Bardsey Island, or Ynys Enlli as it's known in Welsh. I have visited a few times, and am always amazed at its beauty, the ferociousness

Bardsey Island: A refuge for persecuted Christians. The first abbey being built by monks in the sixth century
© *Julius Kielaitis Shutterstock*

of the sea surrounding this tiny island, and the rugged beauty of its nature. I have been there with my sister and friends before, and the quietness of the island is astounding. Midsummer it is beautiful, but at winter the choppiness of the sea can sometimes determine whether you are lucky enough to cross or not. Although it is off the Llyn Peninsula, and not too far from the mainland, when you're on it it really does feel like the middle of nowhere, in the best possible way.

Bardsey has inspired many writers and artists, awestruck at its beauty. But Bardsey Island, you could say, has its spooky side. It is said that 20,000 saints are buried on Bardsey Island, as it was once a popular pilgrimage destination. Although I have never seen the 20,000 souls said to be buried on the island, I believe this incredible so-called myth. The mountain on the island looks to Wales and Ireland, and on it everything seems possible.

In the dead of night, with only the odd seal making a noise and the waves crashing against the island rocks, it's hard not to think of the saints that are said to call Bardsey home. The island is without electricity, only the flashing light of the lighthouse reminding you that there is life elsewhere and nearby. That's the best thing about the island; thinking about how remote, beautiful and alone the island is.

JASPER FFORDE – Out Walking near Rhayader

Jasper Fforde is a novelist known for his Thursday Next novels, but he has also created other series such as The Last Dragonslayer and Shades of Grey. Jasper lives in Wales, as he explains in his story, 'Out Walking'.

This incident happened in the mid 1980s, in a region of Wales just North of Rhayader – an area of rolling hillside, thorn hedge and stunted oak. Mainly sheep-farming and much of it comparatively empty, it is a land so spectacular in its loveliness that entire lives could be spent here without necessary recourse to anywhere else.

The beautiful scenery around Rhayader, the scene of Jasper's ghostly encounter

I live in Wales but consider myself a long-term visitor. My adopted nation, if you will. I like to walk across the hills, but where possible seek the landowner's permission, especially if they have 'a fiery reputation'. There were several hills I wanted to visit in the area, seen from afar, hilltops covered with tight oak forest, so after getting the relevant permission, I set forth into the relative unknown, away from the footpaths and the bridle-paths, off into the hidden world that exists in the heart of Wales that was very much off-grid in the 1980s and to a certain extent still is.

It was a relatively easy walk, and by wending my way up the hillside through dilapidated gates held together with baler-twine, I made my way to a rocky outcrop hidden beneath the oak canopy, where the rocks were covered in moss, and tree roots clung tightly on the rock as though fearful of being carried off in the wind. It was, I think, a glorious spot, and after looking about to see if there was anything of interest, I headed back down the hill.

I was met by two men in an aged Land Rover held together, like the gates and fences, with baler-twine. I must have surprised them as they looked up with a degree of shock and suspicion, and instantly stopped what they were doing. They were dressed shabbily and I suspected that they too – or their trousers at least – may also have been held up by baler-twine.

One was the father, I presumed, of at least seventy years, with a gnarled face that spoke of long hours outside. The second man was quite clearly his son, as they looked very similar. They did not, I confess, appear overjoyed to see me.

'Hello!' I said in as bright and friendly a tone as I could. 'A fine day.' The older of the two said nothing but simply eyed me suspiciously and I saw the younger of them move to the back of the Land Rover, where he stood, as if somehow at readiness for something. It put me very much ill at ease, but I could run fast, so was not fearful of harm – just of confrontation.

'Do you have kites around here?' I asked, hoping the nervousness did not show itself in my voice. 'I saw some buzzards.'

'Oh yes?' said the old man, with the heavy mid-Wales accent that you don't hear so much these days. 'And where you come from today?' I explained as best as I could in a flustered tone that I lived about thirty miles south of here, all the time with the son's eyes boring into me. I knew full well that it really isn't usual to be murdered on a Welsh hilltop, but at the back of my mind there was a feeling that perhaps I might get a thick ear for the wearisome intrusion into their world. It was the eighties, after all. People could do that sort of thing then.

'Private land,' said the farmer, cutting into my hurried explanation of who I was and what I was doing here.

'Trespassing,' said the son, speaking for the first time.

'Oh, I asked permission,' I muttered quickly, 'from P— Farmhouse, down the way.' This altered the old man's demeanour slightly, but not much.

'Oh yes?' he said again, and looked at his son, who gave an imperceptible shake of his head.

'Yes,' I replied. 'I spoke to your wife, I believe.' This was entirely true. I had approached the open kitchen door not two hours before and seen an elderly woman dressed in a flowery pinafore behind the kitchen table, mixing something in a bowl. The kitchen smelled of hot Rayburn, warm bread and washing. I'd asked if I could climb P— Hill and she had nodded agreeable assent.

I explained this to the farmer, who stared at me, the expression on his face moving away from anger, and more towards something that might be construed as friendliness. His son's demeanour, however, moved in the opposite direction.

'That's nonsense, that be!' he said, taking a step forward, one fist clenched tight. I took a step backwards, but the farmer stopped him with a wave of his hand. 'This woman,' he said after a long pause, 'did she say anything?'

'No,' I replied. 'I just asked if I could walk and she nodded.'

'Ah,' he said.

'This is so much rubbish!' said the son in a voice tinged with barely controlled anger.

'Hush, Gethin,' said the old man, then turned back to me, his eyes glistening with tears. 'How did she look? Was she well?' The questioning up until this time had seemed unusual, but just then I suddenly realised where this conversation was heading. I felt the hairs on the back of my neck lift as the old farmer stared into my eyes, not with a sense of anger, but one of loss.

'She looked . . . fine,' I said, my voice sounding strange and thin, 'making something – stuff – I don't know – in a bowl.' He nodded and gave out a short cough, and his son was swiftly at his side, comforting his father. I was now trespassing not on their land, but their grief, and my place was elsewhere.

I made some comment – an apology, I think – and moved away down the hill at a fast pace, without looking back. I was shaking when I returned to my car, and hurriedly left the area.

I didn't go back until last year, almost a quarter of a century later. The farmhouse had changed little, and I guessed the son now farmed here, probably still holding everything together with baler-twine, like his father before him. I thought about knocking on the door to see if he remembered the incident – to ask him whether it had been an elaborate prank to frighten off an unwelcome visitor – but I decided not to approach the kitchen door. If Gethin was out, then I didn't really want to know who might be in.

OWEN SHEERS – A Beach in West Wales

Owen was brought up in Abergavenny. He is an author, poet, playwright and screenwriter. Owen's story happened when he was ten years old and away on holiday with his family in West Wales.

One night I had a nightmare. I dreamt I was crossing a rickety rope bridge with my two brothers, Dilwyn, four years older, and Hywel, nine years younger. Dilwyn had already crossed to the other side. I was following him, holding Hywel's hand. As we edged our way along, stepping squarely in the middle of each wooden plank, I looked down. The river below seemed impossibly far away, no more than a thread of water running between two towering cliffs. I gripped the rope along the side of the bridge and took another step forward. As I did I suddenly, sickeningly, felt the full weight of Hywel's body tug at my arm. The plank behind me had given way. Before I knew it I was on my knees, the bridge swinging wildly beneath me as Hywel dangled above that far-below river, gripping my hand with his, looking up into my face. I shouted for Dilwyn to come and help, but this was a dream world where sound no longer travelled as it should. He didn't come. I felt Hywel's hand slipping from mine, his fingers working to find purchase. I looked down at him, trying to pull him up onto the bridge. But as I pulled his fingers slipped further until, with one last, slow slide, they were no longer there. As he fell he kept his eyes on mine. Wide, shocked, scared. And that was what I woke up with. His eyes, staring up at me as he fell away towards that river.

The next morning, as we had every morning, we went to the beach. It was a beautiful West Wales day. Magnesium bright, a breeze coaxing white flecks from the surf. Dilwyn and I were taking turns to look after Hywel. He'd found a piece of wood stuck between two rocks above a little sandy pool. For the last half-hour I'd been holding his hand as he walked back and forth, back and forth, apparently finding the newness of the experience as fresh and joyful each time. I, however, was becoming fractious. This was my holiday too and I had rock pools to explore, cliffs to climb. I didn't want to be stuck looking after my little brother all day. I shouted to Dilwyn to come and take his turn with Hywel. He pretended not to hear. I shouted again, taking my eyes off Hywel and, as I did, I felt a strange echo of my dream: the sudden weight of his body tugging at my arm, his fingers slipping from mine. As I turned back I saw Hywel falling off the piece of wood. I lunged to catch him as he fell backwards into the pool and, briefly, under the water. Within a second or two I'd pulled him out but just before I did I saw his face – his expression was another perfect echo from my dream. His eyes, wide, shocked, scared, looking up at me.

PHIL RICKMAN – Blossom on the Tree

Phil Rickman has spent most of his adult life in Wales and the border country, where he has won awards for his work as a BBC radio and TV news reporter. Phil is a well-known author, with his novels often dealing with the subject of the paranormal. The Merrily Watkins series, which began with the novel The Wine of Angels, concerns a female priest employed as an exorcist.

With a fictional ghost story, the *was-it-or-wasn't-it?* element is crucial. A ghost story where everything can be proved to be exactly as it seems is, in the end, unsatisfying. The mystery must never be entirely dispelled. And maybe that's important in real life, too.

© Julius Kielaitis Shutterstock

This one goes back to when I was working on *The Wine of Angels*, a rural crime novel with an element of the paranormal. The plot involves apples and orchards and cider-making on the Welsh border. Which is where we live, next to the remains of an orchard with some very old trees, and where, researching folklore relating to orchards, I came across an old rhyme, which goes:

> *If there's blossom on the tree when the apples are ripe*
> *It's a sure termination of somebody's life.*

The very fact that it's a lousy rhyme somehow makes it more sinister. For me anyway. Especially when I went out one August morning to find a single blossom among the ripening apples on the tree nearest the house.

To say it scared me would be overstating it, but my dad wasn't well at the time, and I made a point of asking our oldest neighbour if this was a phenomenon he'd ever encountered before.

'No,' he said. 'Not as I can think of.'

The flower soon disappeared but the image remained. In the country, where nature is closer, these things hang around. Somehow they matter. On a warm evening, a couple of days later, the phone rang.

A Friday night. On Friday nights there would often be a call from one of our oldest friends, also a writer and broadcaster. We'd worked together as young journalists, but now he and his wife lived over a hundred miles away on the Lancashire coast. Still, we kept in touch; we had very similar interests and we laughed at the same things. And he was the closest I've ever had to a mentor – the guy who introduced me to theories about mysteries in the landscape which would inspire several novels.

The call was from his daughter. Our friend had collapsed and died in his garden – heart-related, but there had been no warning signs, although his father had also died young in similar circumstances.

He was only about six years older than I was. I'd never lost a friend like this before. It was like the end of a whole cycle of life and maybe the start of a bleaker one. I spent most of that evening on the phone, to former colleagues. And then, long after dark, I went outside to take it up with the apple tree. Which was when something started to happen.

The bereavement apparition is, apparently, the most common form of . . . well, either paranormal phenomena or psychological projection, depending on where you stand on these issues. Wives see recently dead husbands in their favourite chairs or walking in the garden. Office workers are aware of former colleagues sitting at the next desk. They blink – gone. Imagination. Part of the mourning process.

What happened that night was more oblique; more suggestive, I suppose, of a sense of humour surviving death.

You have to imagine the stillness of the hour before midnight, a late summer warmth in the air, no breeze. A clear sky over the Dutch barn in front of our house, the valley silent. Which made the sudden yipping noise all the more startling. I thought at first, *fox?* But it was far too close, and it kept on, with a cocky stridency, very loud, filling the night. As if it was shouting, 'Well, come *on* . . .'

Above me, the bathroom window opened, my wife calling down.

'What *is* it?'

I didn't know. I'd never heard it before.

I went back into the house to get a torch. Walked across the orchard, shining the beam into the hedge in case something was trapped. All this time, it carried on, a sharp, demanding yelp:

No here. *Here!*

And when I pointed the beam up into one of the fruit trees, there it was.

Occasionally, we hear owls. Always tawny owls, the *to-wit-to-woo* variety. I'd never heard an owl that made this noise, and I'd never seen an owl that looked like this either. Sitting there, spotlit by the torch, it was like a cartoon owl. I think it had ears. It certainly had attitude. It kept on making the noise and holding eye contact with me, from just a few feet away.

About bloody time.

I don't know how long we stood staring at one another, me and the owl. Maybe less than a minute, though it seemed much longer than that. Then the owl went silent and lifted himself off the tree and sailed serenely away over the barn.

In folklore, worldwide, owls are often seen as symbolic of a departing soul.

Well, I knew this, but I still went back to the books to check it out.

Unfortunately, we didn't have a big bird book, but my radio producer did and when I told her the story the following week, describing the owl and its curious call, she went to consult the book.

There are several breeds of owl in the British Isles, but only two seemed to fit. I don't remember which they were and I've avoided looking them up in case the denouement wasn't so perfect after all. But neither of them, my producer said, was native to the Welsh Border.

The one that seemed closest to my owl favoured moorland and sand dunes. We're at least sixty miles from the coast.

But our late friend had lived so close to the sea that he used to walk among the dunes every night.

As for that urgent, demanding call . . . my producer swears that it was described in the book as *rick, rick, rick*.

There you go . . . the owl that was trying to say my name.

Twelve years since that night, and we've never seen or heard anything like it since.

The End